MW00885334

One for Each Night

Also by Marilyn Kallet:

— *Sleeping With One Eye Open: Women Writers and the Art of Survival*, co-edited with Judith Ortiz Cofer, University of Georgia Press, 1999.

— *How to Get Heat Without Fire* (poetry), New Messenger/New Millenium Writings, 1996.

— *Worlds in Our Words: Contemporary American Women Writers*, co-edited with Patricia Clark, Blair Press/Prentice Hall, 1996.

— *A House of Gathering: Poets on May Sarton's Poetry*, (essays), edited by Kallet, University of Tennessee Press, 1993.

— *Honest Simplicity in William Carlos Williams' "Asphodel, That Greeny Flower,"* Louisiana State University Press, 1985.

— *In the Great Night* (poetry), Ithaca House, 1981.

— *Last Love Poems of Paul Eluard*, transl. Kallet, Louisiana State University Press, 1980.

— *Devils Live so Near* (poetry), Ithaca House, 1977.

One for Each Night

Chanukah Tales and Recipes

Marilyn Kallet

Illustrated by Heather Seratt

Celtic Cat Publishing   KNOXVILLE

Copyright © 2003 Marilyn Kallet

All rights reserved. No part of this publication may
be reproduced, stored in a retrieval system, or
transmitted in any form or by any means—
electronic, mechanical, photocopy, recording, or
other—except for brief quotations in written
reviews, without the prior written permission
of the publisher.

Published by Celtic Cat Publishing
Knoxville, Tennessee
www.celticcatpublishing.com

Manufactured in the United States of America
Design by Dariel Mayer
Illustrations by Heather Seratt

ISBN: 0-9658950-4-1
Library of Congress Control Number: 2003106578

For Lou and Heather,
one for each night—

> *One for each night,*
> *they will shed a sweet light*
> *to remind us of days long ago.*
> —Chanukah, Oh Chanukah

Contents

Acknowledgments

I am grateful to Hilda Gross for her generosity in providing many of our tasty holiday recipes.

Our illustrator, Heather Seratt, has added new layers of humor and fantasy to our tales.

Rabbi Beth Schwartz of Temple Beth El was very helpful in answering questions about the ancient meaning of *Chanukah*.

Publisher Jim Johnston of Celtic Cat Publishing has promoted creative writing and multicultural books in Tennessee for many years. His encouragement is deeply appreciated.

"Kugela" and "Lord of the Rugalach" were previously published in *Literary Lunch: An Anthology of the Knoxville Writers' Guild*. "The Matzo Ball" appears in the Spring 2003 issue of *Now & Then: The Magazine of Appalachia*. Grateful acknowledgment is made to the editors.

Preface

Recently at *Chanukah* I found myself broke, flat as a
latke. I knew that my daughter Heather and my
husband Lou would both be searching the mantel-
piece each night for a present. Eight nights of the
holiday, times two—sixteen presents called for—
and no *gelt*!

Using my talents as an English major, I decided to
create homemade presents, to write festive new
stories for each night of Chanukah. The stories
would be about food, of course. And I would cook up
tasty dishes to accompany the tales.

The first night, Lou and Heather were a bit skepti-
cal about receiving stories as gifts, but they entered
into the celebratory spirit as soon as they tasted the
Chanukah treats that I had baked. By the second
night, they were hooked! They both tore open their

envelopes to read fresh adventures. And their mouths watered, since they had quickly figured out that the foods mentioned in the stories would be waiting for them at our table!

Now you hold in your hands eight of the original stories, in this first edition. I hope that you enjoy these tales and recipes. Many of the recipes were provided by my mother-in-law, Hilda Gross, one of the great bakers in Philadelphia, former caterer of desserts, mother of four, and wife of an enthusiastic eater.

Every good cook adds a few creative and original touches to the best recipes, and any good storyteller will lend his or her own inflections to the tales. Let me know how these holiday treats turn out for you, and tell me which spices you decide to add to the Chanukah magic. You can reach me by email: mkallet@utk.edu.

And now, *fressen!*

First Night

Kugela

Once there was a very lovely and *zoftig* young maiden who lived not far from Minsk. The boys of her village had noticed that her skin appeared soft and milky. But Luchshen Kugel—or Kugela, as everyone called her—held herself as aloof as a cat.

One day a handsome strapping fellow named NiceJewishBoy arrived at Kugela's door. NJB was a well-to-do young man with his own beautiful black horse, Impala. "Come with me to the town dance," he pleaded with Kugela. "We'll have a lovely time, and I'll bring you home well before the moon rises too high, before there's any danger of Cossacks!"

Kugela was tempted—it had been so long since she had danced. She couldn't even remember how. Her arms had grown sore from doing the daily chores. She needed to swing them, to loosen her poor muscles.

"I'll go!" she said. "But only if you bring me sweet berries. Blueberries from the forest," she insisted.

"Are you nuts?" responded NJB. "It's winter. Snow has fallen and has covered even the forest. There are no berries to be plucked, my sweet."

Nevertheless, Kugela remained firm. So NJB had to use his wits. He visited the town winemaker and inquired, "Please, my good man, is there any chance that you have saved a few berries from your winemaking? Perhaps you have dried and pressed a handful?"

NJB was in luck. In exchange for some fine fabric cut by his father's hands, he received a fat packet of dried blueberries.

He brought them home and gave them to his mother, who enrobed them in sweet cream from her blue cow. Only then did he present them to his sweetheart. "Kugela, my Kugela," he swooned, "now will you dance with me?"

Lucky Kugela tried to answer him, but her mouth was full and blue. NiceJewishBoy knew—he had always known—that her answer would be "Yes!" To the joyful strains of *klezmer*, they waltzed beneath the moon. Even the Cossacks had sweet dreams that night, dreams of potato pancakes with blueberry maidens twirling on top, on their beautiful blue toes.

Luscious Luchshen Kugel

$1/2$ pound medium noodles, cooked
$1/4$ cup sugar
4 eggs, separated
$1/2$ pound cream cheese
1 can evaporated milk (12 ounces)
2 cups of milk
1 cup golden raisins

Topping:
2 apples, sliced, if desired
$1/2$ cup sugar
1 tablespoon cinammon

In a large bowl, mix noodles, sugar, and egg yolks. In a blender, mix half of the cream cheese with half of the evaporated milk, then repeat the process with the rest of the cream cheese and evaporated milk. Add to the noodle mixture.

Stir in the 2 cups of whole milk and the raisins. (The mixture will be loose). Beat the egg whites until only slightly stiff and fold into the mixture.

Pour into a greased 9 x 11-inch pan. Layer apple slices on top, as desired. Sprinkle with sugar and cinnamon mixture. Place in refrigerator overnight.

Preheat oven to 350°.

Place the noodle pan into a larger pan that has been filled with 1 inch of hot water. Bake in 350° oven about 50 minutes until a knife inserted in the center comes out clean.

Serves 12 generous portions.

Second Night בּ

Lord of the Rugalach

Bubbe was a beautiful little old lady with a secret: she knew the ancient art of restoring human happiness through baking. She practiced good magic, the alchemy of turning humble ingredients into light and golden creations. But Bubbe was growing older, and she feared her art would die out, leaving the earth flat as a flapjack.

Her husband, the great wizard Gasoff, worked in his laboratory deep underground. The secret arts he practiced restored ancient machinery to humming order. He was a brother in the fraternity of tinkerers and engineers, and he was not at all interested in the culinary arts (except in the art of eating).

Bubbe and Gasoff had a beautiful son named Lou. When he was born, he smelled like cinnamon and raisins, like a little loaf of coffeecake.

His parents should have suspected that he was chosen to rise. As a youth, Lou seemed to be interested in his father's workshop rather than in his mother's spells. But as he grew older, he turned more and more to his mother's secret arts. He became an apprentice baker.

"My son," his mother said, when he was old enough to understand, "the world is round like a *challah*, and we bake in order to maintain roundness, both in humans and in the cosmos. If the cake rises, the heavens stay high above, and the humans rest happily at the table. Earth was created at the kitchen table, and we renew its origins daily."

Lou was an eager, gifted student. He could bake a *rugalach* to end all rugalachs. Whenever there was a celebration among the Jewish community, families called upon Lou to bake. Yet there were obstacles. Some felt that Lou should remain true to his mother's recipe, and that he must never, never add raisins. One night, in his sleep, a voice came to Lou: "Louis! Throw the fiery rum-soaked raisins into the mountain of dough!" Lou was deeply perplexed. But he followed the voice, rose and soaked some raisins, and then (as only adults can do), he lit them very carefully over the kitchen sink, and watched until the flames died down. He threw these into the bowl of dough, rolled, twisted, and cut the dough into cookies.

While some of the old witchy women criticized these cookies (*Oy vey!* I'm getting *ein bischen schnockered*—a little dizzy—just from one bite!"), they ate them all up at the next *Oneg Shabbat*.

Lou made his mother proud, and he made all of the *noshers* happy. Though wars continued on earth, some people were always sweet and gentle from their eating of Lou's rugalach. Those people took afternoon naps, and hardly ever quarreled.

Cream Cheese Rugalach

8 ounces cream cheese
1 stick butter
1 stick margarine
2 cups flour and flour for the board
2 teaspoons baking powder
$1/4$ teaspoon salt
$1/3$ cup sour cream
2 eggs (separated)
fruit preserves (not jelly, which will ooze out)
1 tablespoon cinnamon
$1/2$ cup sugar
$1/2$ cup golden raisins, if desired
$1/2$ cup chopped walnuts or pecans, if desired

In a large bowl, cream together the cream cheese,
butter, and margarine. Add 2 egg yolks and $1/3$ cup
sour cream.

Sift together flour, salt and baking powder. Gradually add flour mixture to the cream cheese and
butter mixture until dough forms. Mix thoroughly.

Leave at least 3 hours, or overnight in covered bowl in the refrigerator.

Preheat oven to 330°.

Take the egg whites out of fridge and set aside.

On a floured board, roll out the dough about 1/4-inch thick and cut into approximately 2-inch squares.

Use best quality preserves. Put about 1/2 teaspoon of preserves (and a few nuts and raisins if desired) in the middle of each square. Bring the two ends of the diagonal together, and press.

Beat the 2 egg whites with 1/2 teaspoon of warm water, brush on cookies, and sprinkle with cinammon and sugar.

Place on greased baking sheet. Bake at 330° until golden brown, about 25 minutes.

Makes 36 cookies.

Third Night

The Matzo Ball

All the girls were primping, getting ready for the
Matzo Ball, the biggest social event of the season.
Fancy dress was required. Each girl yearned to be
the lightest, fairest, fluffiest maiden at the dance.
According to tradition, ball gowns were supposed to
dazzle in ivory or white. Shoes could be bleached to
match, and girls might adorn them with sprays of
parsley or celery. Onions were absolutely out of the
question, as they would clash with girlish perfumes.

Poor Heddy! She did not own a gown for the
dance. Worse yet, she had no money, and no time to
earn any.

"Don't worry, darling," her mother comforted her.
"We can find something at Matzo Ball Mall." So they
zipped off to a little-known mall outside of Chicken
Soup Forge, where all of the stores specialized in
second-hand matzo ball clothing and accessories.

"Many great Jewish actresses donate their clothing to the boutiques," her mother explained, "and the profits go to the scholarship fund."

Heddy allowed herself to be coaxed along by her mom. The moment she walked into the first store, Matzo Ball Belles, she saw the very dress she needed. It shimmered round and white and was decked with layers of frothy lace. Everywhere dangling spangles gleamed in the shape of little carrots. (The more carrots, the more valuable the dress.) And wouldn't you know, it fit her like a soup spoon! Searching inside the lining, Heddy found the label: "Made by Calvin Perlmutter Klein for Courtney Lovenut, but worn only once, when she fell off a stool on MTV."

"You were right, Mother," Heddy admitted. "I shouldn't be such a snob. From now on, the thrift shops are for me!"

Heddy glowed like a disco matzo ball on the night of the big dance. She was perfect, a little salty, light on her feet. The boys were stirred and the other girls agreed—Heddy looked absolutely delicious!

My Mother's
Lightweight Matzo Balls

2 tablespoons softened butter
2 eggs, separated
1/2 cup matzo meal
1/2 teaspoon salt
2 tablespoons of soup stock

Beat the egg whites until frothy.
In a medium bowl, mix the butter, egg
whites, and yolks. Add the matzo meal and
the salt until they are well blended. Add the
soup stock and cover the mixing bowl.
Leave covered in the refrigerator overnight.

Roll the batter gently into medium/small
balls—keeping the batter loose. This is the
secret of fluffy matzo balls (if you pack the
balls too tightly, they will be heavy).

In a two or three quart pot, boil lightly salted water (not soup). Reduce heat to bubbling and gently add the matzo balls.

Cook for 30-40 minutes. Then remove and place in your soup. You can reheat them in the soup.

Makes 4 servings.

(I usually triple the recipe, but do not triple the salt.)

Fourth Night

What Mandel Brought

Once there lived a little old baker from
Minsk named Mandel. A hard worker,
he grew very tired of trying to make
bread from old potatoes. What he
really needed was a genie, like those he
had heard about in stories. But he
suspected that genies hardly ever
helped the Jews. Who ever heard of a
genie fighting off the Cossacks, or
pushing bullies off their horses? Did
anyone know of a genie who could stay
up all night baking cakes and bread out
of scraps? Could anyone remember a
genie who had left gold coins for a
poor *hamische* boy, or who had offered
a humble baker a little something nice
to nosh on?

Mandel was fed up with potatoes, bored with black bread that tasted like worn-out shoes. He longed for something sweet and light. Though he didn't mean to, when he lit his holiday candles, he added a special request on top of the Chanukah blessing:

Praise be Thou, O Ruler of all, for permitting us to light the miraculous lamps. Maker of all things, please could you bring me just one tiny little sweet thing to eat? Lord, I will bake an offering to the poor, as well as an offering to my poor shriveled tummy. My baking will always be a prayer unto Thee. O Ruler, forgive my lowly ways and grant me peace, understanding, a snack, and some baking supplies.

Mandel was not feeling very proud of himself when he went to sleep that night. Now he was not only poor and hungry, he had become sacrilegious as well. Yet the Ruler of all, the First Light, took pity on him. When Mandel awakened, there by his candles he found a shiny gold coin, and a package of golden grapes that had been dried and preserved. He thanked the Almighty and began to bake the finest, sweetest *mandelbrot* in the whole of Minsk. First he offered some cake to the poorest folks, then to the rabbi, and only then to his own poor stomach.

Always when he baked, he praised the Lord, and since he did not have eggs, he added laughter and songs for leavening.

Golden Mandelbrot

2 sticks unsalted butter, softened
1 cup sugar
3 eggs, beaten
1 tablespoon freshly ground orange zest
juice of one lemon
1 teaspoon vanilla extract
$1/2$ cup chopped almonds
$3^1/2$ cups flour
$3^1/2$ teaspoons baking powder
1 teaspoon salt
optional: 2 tablespoons of mandarin orange
    liqueur

Preheat oven to 325°.

Cream butter and sugar.

Add beaten eggs, vanilla, lemon juice, orange zest, liqueur, and nuts mixed with a little flour.

Sift together remaining dry ingredients and then gradually add them to the mixture.

Cut dough into three parts and form into rolls.

Bake at 325° for approximately 40 minutes.

Remove from pan, cut into slices 1-inch thick, and return to oven until golden brown.

Makes approximately 30 servings.

Fifth Night

Chanukah Tales from the Crypt

Hannah was a good little girl, but she did not like *tzimmes*. She did not like the way the sliced sweet potatoes lay there in too much syrup. She did not like the way the prunes clumped gloomily between the potato slices. She had never much cared for cooked carrots, and certainly did not fancy them mixed in with other loathsome ingredients. She did not even appreciate the word "stew." So Hannah refused to eat the tzimmes that her mother had worked so hard to prepare.

To make matters worse, Hannah's dad proclaimed, "I have never liked tzimmes. My dear mother never made tzimmes!"

Hannah's mom took away the casserole dish, and stashed it in the refrigerator. "The tzimmes will be back!" she grumbled. Hannah felt goose pimples rise on her arms.

That evening, when she climbed into bed, Hannah thought she heard something at her bedroom window. Though her nightlight had gone out, the moon beamed bright. Then she spied an orange blob at the windowpane! Though it had no eyes, she knew that it was looking for her. With a loud tear, the window screen ripped. *Creak!* The window sash opened. The orange mess started to slither through Hannah's bedroom window!

Hannah screamed so loudly that her cat jumped up and yowled!

The watchcat must have scared away the giant blob of sweet potato, for when Hannah looked again it was gone. The window was closed tight, and the screen no longer had a tear in it. Hannah raced into the kitchen where her mother and father were peacefully reading the newspaper. "I was attacked by a sweet potato!" she yelled.

Hannah's mother accompanied her back to her room, where they checked outside the window and under the bed. No blob! Her mother said, "Maybe you shouldn't try to sleep on an empty stomach. Would you like to have a bedtime snack?"

"Yes," answered Hannah, "as long as it's not orange!"

Her mother offered her some lovely blue potato salad, made with those trendy blue fingerling potatoes that you can find at the Fresh Market in tiny packages for about ten dollars. On the kitchen counter sat some extra spuds, rejects from the salad. They were knobby and gnarled, just like a witch's fingers!

Tzimmes, not Tsuras

(Hassle-Free Sweet Potatoes and Fruit)

2 pounds sweet potatoes or yams
2 medium carrots, parboiled
1 pound prunes, washed
2$\frac{1}{2}$ cups of pineapple pieces (you can use
    fresh pineapple, but you will need juice
    as well)
1 teaspoon salt
brown sugar to taste
pineapple juice from can

Preheat oven to 400°.

Peel sweet potatoes and cut into 1$\frac{1}{2}$-inch slices.

Cut carrots into 1-inch pieces.

Arrange sweet potatoes, carrots, pineapple, and prunes in a rectangular baking dish.

Sprinkle salt and sugar as well as pineapple juice over the top.

Bake in the preheated oven and baste with pineapple juice from time to time. Remove when the sweet potatoes and carrots are soft and brown.

Serves 8.

Sixth Night 1

The Latke Child

Harry was a cheerful, friendly, roly-poly child. Like his dear father, he loved to eat. His mother loved to cook, and so their family hummed along nicely. Every day Harry's mother packed his school lunch box with *latkes*, Harry's favorite food. Along with those little potato pancakes, his mother included a small cup of sour cream and a container of apple sauce.

Now we all know that one can have too much of a good thing. Truth be told, Harry was growing sick of latkes. One day at lunch time he sat next to a classmate named Anna. Anna was nibbling on carrot sticks and celery, apples and mixed nuts. Harry looked over at her lunch, and listened longingly to the crunch of fresh vegetables and fruits.

"I'll trade you a potato pancake for a slice of apple and a couple of almonds," Harry said.

"Sure!" said Anna, who was growing sick of rabbit food. Those latkes smelled so good she could hardly wait to bite into one.

After that, Harry and Anna shared their lunches every day. The combination of foods made them grow happier and healthier. Harry became lean and strong. Anna started to round out in very pleasant ways.

One day, as they were munching companionably, Harry noticed a gold key on the chain around Anna's neck.

"What's that key for?" asked Harry.

"I'm a latch-key child," Anna responded. "My parents both work until 6:00, but I get home from school at 3:00. So I have to let myself in with my key," she said.

"Well, I'm a latke child," exclaimed Harry. They both laughed so hard that they almost forgot to finish their lunches. As it turned out, both children possessed the keys to happiness, since they knew how to make lasting friendships. And they both held the keys to their parents' hearts.

Easy Latkes

6 medium-sized potatoes
2 small onions
2 eggs
4 tablespoons flour
1 teaspoon salt (less can be used)
$^1/_2$ teaspoon baking powder
dash pepper
vegetable oil

Grate six medium-sized peeled potatoes and two small onions. If you are using a hand grater, use the finer blades for nicely textured latkes. Drain off extra liquid. Stir in eggs, flour, salt, baking powder, and a dash of pepper.

Heat $^1/_4$ inch of oil in a frying pan. Oil is ready when a drop of water sizzles in the pan. (Don't let the oil burn).

Gently place tablespoons of the latke batter in the hot oil. Fry on both sides until golden brown.

Drain on paper towels.

Serve hot with sour cream or apple sauce.

If you have mashed potatoes on hand, you can add a few tablespoons to your grated potato batter for fluffier latkes.

Serves 4.

Seventh Night

The Princess and the Pirogi

"Cousin Rosalie is coming for an overnight visit," Sarah's mother announced. "What a lovely girl, so smart and poised! She has style and great taste. In fact, she's a real princess!"

Sarah was five, and she had just finished reading the story, "The Princess and the Pea." She knew that one could test for a real princess by placing a pea under the mattress. But peas seemed much too small to be trustworthy for such a trial. So Sarah decided to use one of the *pirogis* that her father had prepared for dinner. When no one was looking, she borrowed one of those lovely plump potato dumplings and thrust it under the guest mattress, as far as her little arm would go.

Cousin Rosalie arrived at the house looking just like a fashion model. She sat down at the table in time for dessert, and for the singing of Chanukah songs. After their meal, the whole family sang, "Oh Chanukah, Oh Chanukah, come light the menorah!" Everyone arose, held hands and danced the lively *hora*. Soon Rosalie said, "I'd better stop dancing so vigorously. These are new shoes, and I need to pre-serve them." Then she added, laughing, "And now I need my beauty sleep!" Off she went to get ready for bed. Little Sarah began to grow sleepy as well.

In the morning, Rosalie had left for school before Sarah came in for breakfast. Sarah herself had a busy schedule that day, and the next, and so she forgot about the pirogi. Weeks passed before anyone had a reason to go back into the guest room. When her mother went in there to tidy up, she smelled some-thing bad, something like the odor of old gym socks and skunks. But there was nothing in the garbage to cause a smell. She changed the linen, but even that didn't seem to stop the problem.

"Sarah, I just can't imagine where the awful smell in the guest room is coming from!" her mother exclaimed.

Finally Sarah remembered the pirogi, and said to her mother, "Check under the mattress!" Her mother lifted the mattress and there lay a squashed rotting potato dumpling. Her mother scrubbed and sprayed, and then she turned to Sarah for an explanation. Sarah said, "I just wanted to see if Rosalie was a real princess! If the pirogi had kept her awake then we would have known for sure!" Her mother couldn't help but laugh.

"Sarah, there's only one princess in this house, and I'll let you guess who that is!"

Classic Potato Pirogi

Dough:
1$\frac{1}{2}$ *cups flour plus flour for the board*
1$\frac{1}{2}$ *teaspoons baking powder*
1 egg
$\frac{1}{2}$ *cup chicken fat or vegetable shortening*
pinch of salt
$\frac{1}{4}$ *cup of water (approximately)*

Potato filling:
4 medium potatoes, peeled and cooked
1 onion sliced and sauteed
1 cup sliced and sauteed mushrooms

Coating:
egg white mixed with one tablespoon warm
 water

Preheat oven to 350°.

Mix first five ingredients and add just enough water to make a soft dough.

Mash potatoes and mix with onions and mushrooms for filling.

Roll dough out about $1/8$-inch thick and cut into $3^1/2$-inch circles.

Fill each circle with 1 tablespoon of potato mixture. Fold each in half and pinch edges together. Prick with a fork.

Bake in greased pan at 350° for about 35 minutes until brown. Coat with egg white and water mixture for the last few minutes. May be frozen.

Makes approximately 15 pirogis.

Eighth Night

Mo and the Dancing Bear

Mo and his family lived in the Village of Kreplach-Eaters, not too far from Old Minsk. As you know, *kreplach* is a noodle dumpling, filled with chopped meat. The Chinese call these *won tons*, and they roll the dough until it's smooth. Jewish grandmothers make these wrappers wrinkly to resemble the faces of newborns and of very old men. Either way, they're delicious, and everyone in Mo's village loved them, though in hard times it was difficult to find meat for the fillings.

Mo was nine-years-old, and restless. He yearned to hike through the woods. He had become a good woodsman, but it was October and the snow had been falling for weeks. "I'll leave a trail of kreplach, so my family can find me," he thought. The kreplach from the night before had been almost empty inside, with only a bit of meat in each one.

Mo set out through the woods, marking his path with kreplach. A big old bear smelled those dumplings and began to follow Mo's tasty trail. That bear devoured every one of those near-empty kreplachs, and then he started growling for more. Mo turned around and beheld the giant brown creature. Quickly he pulled his harmonica from his pocket, and began to play a Yiddish tune. The bear blinked, smiled, and started to lift his huge paws. As long as Mo played, the bear jigged. Mo kept up the lively music all the way home.

Now Mo was the owner of a dancing bear. He named her Klezmer. His family was distressed—another mouth to feed, and a huge one at that! But soon it became clear that Klezmer was a lucrative attraction. Mothers and fathers brought their children to watch the bear dance, and even a few Cossacks snuck away from the castle to observe. Most of the spectators left a coin or a loaf of pumpernickel or something else good to eat.

Sometimes when Mo played the harmonica, he jigged along with the bear. One day, a little girl said loudly, "Mama, that bear is a better dancer than Mo!" Unfortunately Mo heard this, and his pride was wounded. When he danced, he tapped his toes faster and swung his arms wider than than ever before, but now he had doubt in his mind.

In those days, if anyone had a question, he or she consulted the rabbi. The smartest rabbi in Minsk was due to visit Mo's village the next day. So Mo led Klezmer to visit the sage. Politely, Mo asked the frightened rabbi, "Wise one, which of us is the better dancer?" Then Mo blew a lively klezmer tune and danced beside Klez.

"You make excellent partners!" the rebbe pro-nounced. "Put on a silly cap, tie a matching scarf around the bear's neck, and soon your fame will spread far and wide." And that's exactly what Mo did. Mo and Klezmer danced for the crowds every Sunday at 4:30, and the bear always performed beautifully—as long as he was served kreplach and a nice slice of coffeecake afterward.

Chef Hilda's Bulkas (Coffeecake Rolls)

2 yeast cakes dissolved
      in 1 cup warm water
      until foamy
2¹/₂ cups milk, scalded
³/₄ cup unsalted butter
2 cups sugar
2 eggs, beaten
6¹/₂ cups flour (approx)
1 teaspoon salt
¹/₂ cup white raisins

For the board:
1 cup sugar mixed with
2 tablespoons cinnamon

Warm your oven and then turn off.

In a double boiler, scald 2¹/₂ cups of milk until skin forms on top, and allow to cool to a little warmer than lukewarm.

While the milk is cooling, cream butter with 2 cups sugar.

In another bowl, sift 2 cups of flour and salt.

Add 2 beaten eggs to the warm yeast mixture. Then add the warm milk, 1/2 cup at a time, alternating with the flour until you have sticky dough (will take about 5 cups of flour). Knead it until it comes off of your hands, like bread dough.

Place in 2 buttered bowls, loosely covered with damp towels, and set in the warm oven until it doubles in bulk (about 2 hours).

Take out the bowls and punch down the dough. Cover a rolling board with cinnamon-sugar mixture. Take a handful of dough, stretch to 8 inches long, and then roll in sugar mixture. Twist and roll again in sugar mixture. Put twists in greased pans, not too close together, and place in warm oven again (oven is off) until it doubles in bulk. (Or you can leave overnight in a warm kitchen).

Bake at 350° for about 30 minutes until lightly brown.

Makes 20 ample *bulkas*.

Bear-Baiter's Kreplach

Dough:
1 egg
$^1/_8$ teaspoon salt
$^2/_3$ cup flour (approximately)

Filling:
$^1/_2$ pound of cooked meat
1 slice of onion
salt and pepper to taste
1 teaspoon chicken fat
1 egg

Run the meat through the food processor with the onion, spices, chicken fat, and one egg.

Mix the other egg with salt and flour and knead until elastic. Roll out thin and cut into 2-inch squares. Put a small ball of meat into the center of each square. Fold one corner diagonally to form a triangle, and press the edges firmly together. Work quickly or dough will become too dry.

Let *kreplach* stand for about ten minutes, then drop into boiling soup and let cook for 30 minutes.

If you want to serve these as appetizers, boil them in salt water, drain, and slip them into a hot oven to brown.

Makes approximately one dozen *kreplachs*.

And one for the shamos:

Blue and White Chanukah Cake

Cookie crust:
2 cups of crushed vanilla wafers
$^1/_4$ cup of granulated sugar
$^1/_2$ teaspoon of ground cinnamon
6 tablespoons of melted butter

Cake:
1 8-ounce package of cream cheese,
    room temperature
1 cup sugar
1 teaspoon vanilla
2 large eggs
$1^1/_2$ cups of all-purpose flour
2 teaspoons baking powder
2 cups of blueberries, fresh or frozen
$^1/_2$ cup coarsely chopped white chocolate
confectioner's sugar

Preheat oven to 350°.

To make crust, mix together the crust ingredients, and pat into the bottom of a 9-inch square pan. Bake at 350° for 12 minutes. Set aside. Leave the oven on for the cake.

In a large bowl, blend sugar, cream cheese, and vanilla with an electric mixer. Beat the eggs until frothy and add them to the mixture.

Sift together flour and baking powder. Add to the mixture. With a sturdy wooden spoon very gently fold in the berries and the white chocolate.

Spread batter over the crust. Bake at 350° until cake springs back when lightly touched in center, and looks golden brown, about 50 minutes.

Dust with powdered sugar, using a doily to make lacy patterns on the cake. Remove the doily. Serve warm or cold.

Serves 10 large portions.
(Adapted for Chanukah from *My Body My Diet*)

Glossary of Yiddish and Hebrew terms:

Chanukah (Han-oo-kah): Jewish Festival of Lights, occurs in the Hebrew month of Kislev, which falls in November or December. According to ancient Jewish tradition, eight days were always required to sanctify holy ground. In the year 167 B.C., a small band of Jewish soldiers, the Maccabees, were victorious over the Assyrians, who had desecrated the holy Temple by bringing in animals. Judah Maccabee, son of the priest Mattathias, led the long battle for liberation. On the 25th day of Kislev, after cleaning the Temple, Judah rededicated the sanctuary and lit sacred candles. Talmudic lore recounts that Judah could find only one small container of purified holy oil, enough for one night. Miraculously, that oil lasted for eight nights, hence the nightly lighting of our candles in thanksgiving.

---

bulkas (**bul**-kas): coffeecake rolls
challah (**hal**-lah): round or braided egg bread made for
    Shabbat and for holidays

ein bischen schnockered (ine **bish**-en **shnock**-ered): a little drunk

fressen (**fres**-sen): Chow down!

gelt (gelt): money

hamische (**hay**-mish-a): down-to-earth guy, homey

hora (**ho**-ra): Israeli folk dance, performed at celebrations

klezmer (**klez**-mer): traditional Yiddish music from Eastern Europe, often lively and celebratory, featuring woodwinds, accordians, fiddles, and percussion

kreplach (**krep**-lock): dumpling

latkes (**lat**-keys): potato pancakes

luchshen kugel (**luck**-shen **koo**-ggel): noodle pudding

mandelbrot (**man**-dul braht): almond cookie; biscotti

matzo ball (**mah**-tza ball): round dumplings made with matzo meal rather than with flour, usually served at Passover, or any special holiday

menorah (men-**or**-ah): Originally a seven-branched candleholder in the Temple at Jerusalem, this special nine-branched candelabra is a primary symbol for *Chanukah*. Its candles commemorate the miracle of eight nights, when candles shone brightly in the purified Temple. The ninth candle is for the *shamos*, or "servant" candle, which is usually located higher than the others.

nosh (nahsh): snack

noshers (**nah**-shers): those who snack

Oneg Shabbat (**oh**-neg shah-bat): Literally, "taking delight in the Sabbath." The congregation gathers for blessings and socializing after temple services. It has become a tradition to serve refreshments, including ample sweets.

oy vey! (**oy vay**): exclamation, in this case, "wow!"

pirogi (peer-**oh**-ggi): Eastern European potato or meat dumpling

rebbe (**reh**-bee): rabbi

rugalach (**rugg**-a-lock): cinnamon and raisin cookie

Shabbat (shah-**bat**): Hebrew for "resting." The Sabbath commemorates the seventh day of creation. It begins on Friday evening at sundown and lasts through Saturday at sundown.

shamos (**shah**-mos): Hebrew for "servant" candle, used to light the other eight

tzimmes (**sim**-mess): sweets, in this case a sweet stew

tzuras (**tsoo**-ras): Yiddish for "troubles"

zoftig (**zahf**-tigg): Yiddish for "pleasantly plump"

About the author and illustrator:

Marilyn Kallet received her Ph.D. in Comparative Literature from Rutgers University. She is Professor of English at the University of Tennessee, where she holds the Hodges Chair for Distinguished Teaching and directs the Creative Writing Program. Kallet is the author of eight other books, including poetry, translations, anthologies, and criticism. Her poems have been published in *Prairie Schooner, Sport Literate, New Letters, Tar River Poetry,* and many other magazines. In 2000, the Knoxville YWCA named her Outstanding Woman in the Arts. Dr. Kallet is the poetry editor of *New Millenium Writings.*

Heather Seratt received her Master's degree in English with creative writing emphasis from the University of Tennessee. This is her first illustrated book.